W. SOMERSET MAUGHAM

A Marriage of Convenience and Other Stories

Retold by D. R. Hill

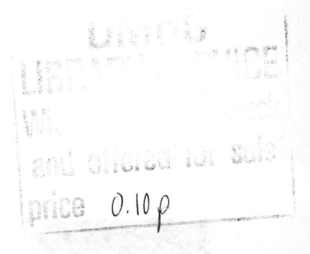

HEINEMANN ELT

INTERMEDIATE LEVEL

Series Editor: John Milne

The Heinemann ELT Guided Readers provide a choice of enjoyable reading material for learners of English. The series is published at five levels – Starter, Beginner, Elementary, Intermediate and Upper. At **Intermediate Level**, the control of content and language has the following main features:

Information Control
Information which is vital to the understanding of the story is presented in an easily assimilated manner and is repeated when necessary. Difficult allusion and metaphor are avoided and cultural backgrounds are made explicit.

Structure Control
Most of the structures used in the readers will be familiar to students who have completed and elementary course of English. Other grammatical features may occur, but their use is made clear through context and reinforcement. This ensures that the reading, as well as being enjoyable, provides a continual learning situation for the students. Sentences are limited in most cases to a maximum of three clauses and within sentences there is a balanced use of simple adverbial and adjectival phrases. Great care is taken with pronoun reference.

Vocabulary Control
There is a basic vocabulary of approximately 1,600 basic words. Help is given to the students in the form of illustrations which are closely related to the text.

Glossary
Some difficult words and phrases in this book are important for under-standing the story. Some of these words are explained in the story, some are shown in the pictures, and others are marked with a number like this ...[3] Words with a number are explained in the Glossary on page 55.

Contents

A Note About the Author

William Somerset Maugham is one of the most famous British writers.

Maugham was born in Paris in 1874. He studied medicine to become a doctor. His first book, called *Lisa of Lambeth*, was published in 1896. It was successful and many copies were sold.

Maugham decided not to work as a doctor, but to be a writer instead. He wrote a great number of books and plays. And many of his stories were about the people he met on his travels all over the world.

Maugham became a rich man. Eighty million copies of his books were sold while he was alive.

Somerset Maugham died in Cap Ferrat, France, on 16th December 1965. He was 91 years old.

A MARRIAGE OF CONVENIENCE

I first saw the small Frenchman and his very large wife as the ship was getting ready to leave Bangkok. I was on my way from Bangkok to Hong Kong and I had boarded[1] the small ship early in the morning.

As I waited for the ship to leave harbour, I saw the Frenchman and his wife arrive. They were the last passengers to board the ship. As they got on to the ship, the captain greeted the small man in French.

From the captain's greeting, I understood that the small man was a French Colonial Governor[2] and that the large lady was his wife.

The ship left the harbour as soon as the Governor and his wife were on board. I went down with the other passengers to the small dining-room for lunch. There were very few passengers and we all ate together at one table with the captain.

The Governor and his wife sat side by side and they looked a strange couple. He was a small man, fat and ugly. He had a round face and a bald head. His wife was very tall and she sat up straight in her chair. They were both about the same age, about fifty-five.

The Governor was an amusing person and talked a lot at lunch. His wife did not talk at all, but I saw that she was very much in love with her husband. From time to time, they held each other's hands under the table. They seemed to be very happily married.

After lunch, we all went off to our cabins[3]. We slept during the heat of the afternoon. In the evening, we all met once again for dinner. Again, the Governor talked amusingly and his wife sat quietly beside him. They held hands from time to time, and they smiled at each other happily.

After dinner, we all went up on deck[4]. I sat down and looked out over the sea. It was a lovely night. The sky was full of bright stars. It was a night for love and romance. The Governor and his wife thought so too. They walked up and down the deck together, holding hands. At first, I thought this was rather funny. But it was also pleasant to see an older married couple who were still in love with each other.

After a while, they stopped and sat down beside me. They were still holding hands. The Governor was silent for some time. This was unusual for him. At lunch and at dinner, he had kept us all amused with his interesting conversation. At last, he spoke.

'Monsieur,' he began. 'Today is an important day in my life. Today is our anniversary[5]. It is the anniversary of the day on which I first saw my wife. And it is also the anniversary of the day on which she promised to be my wife.'

I did not say anything. There was nothing unusual about that. It is not strange for someone to meet his wife on one day and then ask her to marry him on the same day a year later. But the Governor went on with his story.

'I know what you're thinking, Monsieur,' he said. 'You're thinking that there is nothing unusual about that. But you are wrong. It was unusual. I met my wife and I asked her to marry me on the same day.'

I was surprised. Yes, that was very unusual.

'You always bore[6] people with that story,' said his wife. But she smiled as she spoke. I saw that she was happy to hear the story once again.

'Our marriage was a marriage of convenience[7],' said the Governor.

'That's true,' interrupted[8] his wife. 'It was a marriage of convenience. But sometimes love comes after marriage. It is better when love comes after marriage – it lasts longer.'

And as she spoke, she held her husband's hand lovingly.

'Let me explain, Monsieur,' the Governor went on. 'I joined the French navy when I was a young man. I spent many years in the

'Our marriage was a marriage of convenience.'

navy and I retired[9] when I was forty-nine. I was still strong and healthy. I wanted to do something else in life before I was too old.

'Fortunately, I had a cousin who had an important job in the Government. He was able to help me. After a short wait, I went to meet the Minister to the Colonies[10]. He asked me if I wanted the job of Governor of a colony. The colony was far from France, but that did not worry me. I accepted the job happily.

'The Minister told me that I must leave after a month. I told him that I was ready to leave immediately. I was unmarried and had no family to care for.

"You are a bachelor!" said the Minister, looking very surprised. "In that case, you cannot have the post. The new Governor must be a married man."

'I begged him to let me have the job. But he refused. Finally, I said to the Minister, "Is there anything I can do to get this job?"

"Yes, there is," he replied. "You can get married."

"But how can I get married?" I asked. "I am forty-nine years old and I do not know any ladies."

"That's easy" replied the Minister. "Put an advertisement[11] in the newspapers. If you come back here after a month and you are married, you can have the job. But no wife, no job."

'What did you do?' I asked.

'I did not know what to do,' said the Governor. 'I left the Minister's office feeling very unhappy. I wanted the job. I knew the colony. There was not much work to be done and the salary was good.

'Suddenly I knew what I had to do. I walked to a newspaper office. I put an advertisement in the newspaper.'

The small Frenchman leant forward. He took my arm and spoke to me quietly.

'Do you know how many replies I got to my advertisement?' he asked me.

'I've no idea at all,' I replied.

'It is difficult to believe,' said the Governor. 'I still find it

8

difficult to believe. I had exactly four thousand, three hundred and seventy-two replies. They all arrived at the newspaper office and I had to get a taxi to take them to my hotel.

'I did not know what to do. I tried to read them all. I spent three days reading the letters. I looked at the photographs which came with them. Some of the letters were from ladies who had never been married. Some were from widows whose husbands had died. Some were wealthy, some were poor. They were of all ages from seventeen to seventy.'

'How amazing!' I said. 'So you were able to choose your wife from an advertisement.'

'No! No!' he replied. 'There were so many letters that I did not know what to do. There were letters all over the floor and over the chairs and the bed. How could I choose one from so many? Did I have to meet every one of them? I had to find a wife in a month. There was not enough time to meet so many ladies.'

'So what did you do next?' I asked.

'I sat in a café and felt miserable. I did not know what to do. After a time, a friend passed by the café and saw me. He came and sat down beside me.

"Why are you looking so sad?" he asked me. You are usually a happy man."

'I told my friend the story. He laughed and laughed when I told him about the letters lying around everywhere in my hotel room. I started to become angry.

"This is important," I said to him. Why are you laughing? I want to get the job."

My friend stopped laughing.

"Do you really want to get married?" he asked me.

"Of course I do," I replied angrily. "I want to get married. And I want to get married in two weeks' time."

"Stop being angry with me," he said. "And listen carefully. I have a cousin who lives in Geneva. She is Swiss. She comes from a good family. She is the same age as you and she is not ugly. She

'There were letters all over the floor and over the chairs
and the bed.'

has never been married because she has had to look after her sick mother. Her mother is now dead and my cousin is free to marry."

"But will your cousin want to marry me?" I asked my friend. "I am not handsome. In fact, I am quite ugly."

"It does not matter if you are ugly or not," my friend told me. You can never know what a woman wants. Why don't you go to Geneva and ask her? It's easier to go to Geneva than to interview four thousand, three hundred and seventy-two women."

'To cut a long story short, Monsieur,' the Governor continued, 'I took my friend's advice. We went together and bought a large box of chocolates. I took the night train to Geneva.

'Next morning, I went to a hotel and sent the lady a note. I said in the note that I was a friend of her cousin's. I had brought with me a box of chocolates to give to her. I asked her when she could see me.

'She replied immediately and said she would see me in the afternoon at four o'clock.

'As the clock struck four, I knocked at her door and it opened. I was very surprised, Monsieur. In front of me stood a beautiful woman.

'I was so nervous[12] and I nearly dropped the box of chocolates,' the Governor continued. 'I went in and sat down. I handed over the box of chocolates. I gave her news of her cousin in Paris. We talked for about a quarter of an hour. I found her pleasant and interesting.

'I was still very nervous. But I had to speak out. I had to tell her why I had come to see her.'

"Mademoiselle," I said, "I have not come here to give you a box of chocolates. I have come here to ask you to marry me."

She immediately stood up. She looked at me with amazement in her eyes.

"Monsieur," she said at last, you must be mad."

"Please let me explain," I said.

And before she could say another word, I told her my story.

'She looked at me with amazement in her eyes.'

When I told her about the replies to my advertisement, she laughed and laughed.

"Are you telling the truth?" she asked me. "Do you really want to marry me?"

"Mademoiselle," I replied, "I have never wanted anything so much in my life."

"I must have time to think about it," she said.

"I'm sorry, Mademoiselle," I replied. "But I have not got any time. If you will not marry me, I must hurry back to Paris. I will have to look again at that huge pile of letters waiting there for me."

"But I cannot give you an answer immediately," she repeated. "I must think about it. I must discuss it with my friends and my family."

"Mademoiselle," I said. "You do not need to discuss it with anyone. I have told you everything. You are an intelligent woman. There is no time to think about it. You must give me your answer now."

"But this is madness, Monsieur! " she cried. "You want me to give you a reply this very minute?"

"That is exactly what I want you to do," I said. "My train leaves for Paris in two hours' time."

'She looked at me thoughtfully.

"You are quite mad," she said.

"What is your answer?" I asked. "Yes or no?"

'After a moment, she gave me her answer. It was yes.

'And there she is sitting beside you, Monsieur,' the Governor said. 'We were married a fortnight later and I became Governor of a colony. I married the most wonderful wife, Monsieur. A beautiful, amusing and intelligent woman.'

'Don't be foolish,' his wife interrupted. 'You are making us both look foolish in front of this gentleman.'

'Are you a bachelor, Monsieur?' the Governor asked me. 'If you are, I suggest you go to Geneva. The city is full of beautiful, amusing and intelligent women. Anyone who is looking for a wife will find the woman they want in Geneva.'

It was an amazing story. And it was wonderful to see that the two of them were so happily married.

'I can see that your marriage has been very successful,' I said. 'Can you tell me the secret of your success?'

It was the Governor's wife who answered my question.

'The truth is this,' she said. 'In a marriage of convenience, you do not expect to find love and happiness. And so you are not disappointed if you do not find them.

'Love is not the best beginning to a marriage. For two people to be happy in marriage, they must respect[13] each other. They must have similar family backgrounds and similar interests. Then, there is no reason why their marriage should not be as happy as ours.'

And it was the Governor's wife who had the last word.

'Of course,' she said. 'You must remember that my husband is a most remarkable man.'

GERMAN HARRY

A few years ago, I was visiting some of the islands in the Torres Straits. The Torres Straits are near the north-eastern coast of Australia.

I was on Thursday Island and I wanted to go to New Guinea. Boats did not usually go from Thursday Island to New Guinea. So I had to find a boat that would take me there.

I asked the pearl[14] fishermen down in the harbour. They told the skipper[15] of a pearl fishing boat about me. This skipper was ready to take me to New Guinea.

The skipper and his crew of four islanders loaded the small boat with food for the long trip.

A few days before we left Thursday Island, a man came up to me in my hotel. He was carrying a bag of flour and a bag of rice and some magazines.

'Can you stop at the island of Trebucket?' the man asked me. 'These things are for German Harry. Can you take them to him?'

'Of course,' I replied. 'Does this man live on Trebucket?'

'Yes, German Harry lives on Trebucket,' the man replied. 'He has lived alone on Trebucket for the past thirty years. He's a hermit.'

I immediately wanted to know more about German Harry. Who was this strange man who had lived alone on a small island for thirty years? Why did he live such a lonely life?

The pearl fishermen called him German Harry, but they did not think he was German. They thought he was Danish. But they were not sure. The pearl fishermen took food and other things to him whenever they went near Trebucket.

I asked the pearl fishermen about him. They told me a strange story – a very strange story.

Thirty years ago, German Harry worked on a sailing ship. The ship carried goods and passengers to the islands which are all around here. Some of these islands, like Trebucket, are very small and few boats ever go to them.

The ship that German Harry worked on sank in a storm. Sixteen men got away from the sinking ship into two small boats. They were in the small boats for three days and three nights. Finally they landed at Trebucket.

The small boats were wrecked[16] on the rocks round the island and sank. But the men swam safely to the shore. Sixteen men landed safely on the island.

They waited there on the island of Trebucket. They looked out to sea every day. They hoped to see a ship coming to rescue them. They waited and waited, but it was three years before a

ship came.

And when the ship arrived, there were only five men on the island.

'What happened to the other eleven men?' I asked the pearl fishermen.

'No one knows,' was the only reply I got to this question.

The captain of the ship found five men still alive on Trebucket. The captain took four of the men on his ship. They sailed with him and were taken to Sydney in Australia. But German Harry refused to leave Trebucket.

Germany Harry said that he never wanted to live among men again. He had seen terrible things in those three years on Trebucket. He wanted to stay on Trebucket by himself. He wanted to live alone for the rest of his life.

What were the terrible things he had seen?

I asked the pearl fishermen to tell me more. But that was all they knew about German Harry.

The night before we left Thursday Island, I could not sleep. I lay awake thinking about German Harry and those three long years on the island of Trebucket. What had happened? What were the terrible things he had seen?

Had there been a fight on the island? I wondered. Had those eleven men been killed in the fight? Or had something more terrible happened?

I remembered stories about men who had been left on islands where there was no food at all. The stories were horrible. Sometimes the men were starving to death. They had to eat human flesh to stay alive. Was this what had happened to German Harry's companions? Had they been killed and eaten?

We set sail for Trebucket the next day. It was a long slow journey. One evening, after we had been sailing for six days, the skipper told me more about German Harry.

'We'll reach Trebucket tomorrow morning,' he said. 'You can give those things to German Harry.'

'Can't you tell me any more about this strange man?' I asked the skipper. 'How is he able to live on such a small island?'

'Pearls were discovered in the sea near Trebucket,' the skipper said. 'The pearl fishermen came to the island. Harry got an old boat and fished for pearls too. Harry sold his pearls to the pearl fishermen for food and tobacco.

'Then the war started. It was too dangerous for the pearl fishermen to go out in their boats. For five years, Harry lived alone. He saw no one. He lived on fish and sometimes he caught a turtle[17].

'He had a difficult time when he finished all his matches.'

'What did he do then?' I asked.

'He had to keep his fire alight all the time,' the skipper replied.

18

'Harry sold his pearls to the pearl fishermen for
food and tobacco.'

'He woke up every two hours during the night to put more wood on the fire.

'The war ended after five years and the pearl fishermen came back to Trebucket.'

'Did he wonder why no one had come to Trebucket for so many years?' I asked the skipper. 'What did he say to the first visitors after the war?'

'He did not say very much,' the skipper replied. 'He was not interested when the pearl fishermen told him about the war. He thought that men were terrible. The terrible things that happened in the war did not surprise him.'

'Has he ever told anyone what happened to the eleven men who died?' I asked.

'Some pearl fishermen tried to make him talk,' replied the skipper. 'They wanted to find out what had happened during those three terrible years. Also, they believed that Harry had found many valuable pearls. They believed he had hidden them somewhere on the island. The pearl fishermen wanted to find out where he had hidden them.

'They tried to make him drunk. Then they asked him what had happened to the other eleven men. And they asked him where he had hidden his pearls.

'But Harry did not tell them anything. He got angry and walked away.'

I wanted very much to meet this strange man. He had lived on a lonely island by himself for thirty years. What had he thought about all those years? What had he learnt about life? Did he still think that men were terrible?

We reached Trebucket early the next morning. It was a very small island. It was flat with tall coconut trees growing everywhere.

We loaded the bags of flour and rice and the magazines into a small rowing boat. Then we rowed to the shore.

I saw a little hut under the coconut trees. As we came nearer,

Harry appeared and walked slowly down to the shore. We shouted a greeting, but he did not reply.

He was a man of over seventy. He was completely bald and had a long grey beard. His bald head and his face were burnt brown by the sun. His clothes were old, but they were neat and clean.

We followed Harry to the small hut where he lived. There was a bed in the hut, a table and some chairs. There was a table and a bench under a tree near the hut.

He did not seem pleased to see us. We gave him the bags and magazines, but he did not say thank you. He was silent and looked sad. He was not interested in any news from the outside world. The only thing he cared about was his island.

He asked the skipper who I was. He wanted to know what I was doing on the island. Had I come to steal his coconuts? That was all he was interested in. He was not interested in anything except his coconuts, his dogs and his chickens.

But he was interested for a moment in one piece of news. The skipper told him about the death of an old friend. Harry had known the man for a long time.

'Old Charlie dead? That's too bad. Old Charlie dead.'

He said this again and again.

'Old Charlie dead. That's too bad.'

I asked him if he read a lot. But he was not interested in me or in my questions.

'Not much,' he replied and said no more.

Harry had lived alone on this island for thirty years. He had had the beautiful sea and the blue sky around him every day of those thirty years. But he had learnt nothing from the beauty around him. It had not made him wise or happy. He was a mean old man, thinking only of himself and of his coconuts.

I looked into his pale blue eyes. I thought about those three terrible years. What had happened then? What horrors had those eyes seen?

No one now will ever know the truth. I knew what was going to happen.

One day a pearl fisherman will arrive at the island, I thought to myself. Harry will not come down to the shore. The pearl fisherman will walk up to the hut and find Harry lying dead on his bed.

Perhaps the pearl fisherman will search everywhere for the pearls that Harry has hidden. But the pearl fisherman will not find them. No one will ever find those pearls.

Harry will die alone. No one will ever live again on the island of Trebucket. No one will ever know the truth about those three terrible years.

THE LOTUS EATER

In 1913, I visited a friend who lived on the island of Capri. Capri is a most beautiful island in the Bay of Naples. From the island, you can see across the water to Mount Vesuvius on the mainland of Italy.

One day, I went for a walk with my friend. On the way, we passed a man sitting on the hillside looking out at the sea. The man was about fifty and he was dressed in old clothes. He had grey hair and his face was burnt brown by the sun.

'That's Thomas Wilson,' my friend said. 'He's going to die when he's sixty.'

I stopped and looked at my friend.

'That's a strange thing to say,' I told him. 'How does he know he's going to die when he's sixty?'

'Because he's going to kill himself,' my friend replied. 'He came to Capri when he was thirty-five. He has enough money to last for twenty-five years. When his money is finished, he's going to kill himself.'

Wilson did not look very interesting, but I wanted to meet him. I thought he would be an interesting man to talk to. He had made a decision that very few people make. Most people live simple lives. They do not make big decisions which change their lives completely. And very few people decide when they are going to die.

A few days later, I had a chance to have a long talk with Wilson. My friend had invited him to come and have dinner with us. But that evening, my friend was not feeling very well. So Wilson and I had dinner by ourselves. After dinner, we sat in the garden and looked at the beautiful Bay of Naples in the moonlight.

*We sat in the garden and looked at the beautiful Bay of Naples
in the moonlight.*

'This is the most beautiful place in the world,' said Wilson. 'I fell in love with this island the first moment I saw it. That was sixteen years ago.

'I was on holiday in Italy at the time. I took a boat from Naples to visit Capri for a few days. And I fell in love with the place immediately.

'The first night I was here, I sat on the hillside and looked across the Bay. I could see the red smoke coming from the top of Vesuvius.

'Next morning, I went swimming in the bright, clear water. After a swim, I went walking round the island. That day was the Feast of the Assumption[18]. There was a procession going through the streets. The crowd of people following the procession were laughing, dancing and singing. Everyone was happy.

'I stayed here for three days. On my last night, I went for a walk to see the Bay of Naples by moonlight. It was a full moon that night – the same as it is now. And it was on that walk in the moonlight that I made my decision.

'I decided that I was going to live here for the rest of my life.'

'What about your family?' I asked.

'I had no family,' replied Wilson. 'My wife and my daughter were dead. I had no other relations and no close friends.'

'But what about your work?'

'After my first visit here I went back to work in London,' Wilson replied. 'I was a bank manager and I had worked in the same bank since I was seventeen. I did not want to do the same work for the rest of my life. I wanted to go back and live on Capri for the rest of my life.'

'But I did not decide in a hurry,' Wilson went on. 'I had to be sure that I was not making a terrible mistake. So I went on working in the bank for a whole year. That's the one thing I regret[19] now.'

'And you have no other regrets?' I asked.

'None at all,' he replied. 'I thought about it very carefully during that year. If I stayed working at the bank, I would go on doing the same thing day after day, year after year. I would be manager of the same small bank until I retired.

'I kept thinking about Capri – about the sun and the sea and the moonlight. I would die one day like everyone else. I decided I was going to live a happy life before I died.'

'But what about money? Did you have enough money to leave work and come here?'

'I had some money,' replied Wilson. 'I had some savings and I sold my house in London. With this money, I bought an annuity[20] for twenty-five years. Each year, I get enough money to live a simple life. But the money will come to an end after twenty-five years. So, when I am sixty, I will have no more money. That will be the end.'

He did not say exactly what he was going to do when the money was finished. But I understood what he planned to do. I felt a cold shiver running through me. But, it was his own life and he could do what he liked with it.

Before he left that night, Wilson asked me if I'd like to see his house. So, two or three days later, I went to see him. He lived in a small cottage. The cottage was in a vineyard, far from the town. There was a beautiful view from the cottage out over the sea. There was a huge flowering tree beside the door of the cottage. The tree was covered with large, brightly coloured flowers. It looked beautiful.

Inside the cottage there were two rooms and a small kitchen. There was also a shed[21] where he kept firewood. The sitting-room was comfortable, with two large chairs, a desk and a piano. There was also a bookshelf filled with books.

'I found this cottage when I first came back to Capri,' Wilson told me. 'And I have stayed here ever since. It belongs to the owner of the vineyard and his wife comes in every day. She cleans the rooms and she cooks my meals.'

'I see you have a piano,' I said. 'Will you play something?'

The cottage was in a vineyard, far from the town.

He played some music by Beethoven. He did not play very well. But I saw that he enjoyed playing the piano.

I looked round the room and saw a pack of cards. They were old and dirty.

'Do you play cards?' I asked him.

'A lot,' he replied. 'I play patience by myself.'

I now knew everything about Wilson. He lived a quiet life. He bathed in the sea, he went for long walks, he played cards and he read books. He was happy to be by himself, but he also enjoyed meeting people from time to time. Then he would talk quite interestingly.

He lives a dull life, I thought. But he seems to be happy.

————

My visit to Capri came to an end and I went back to England. A year later, in 1914, the First World War broke out. When the war ended, I was busy visiting many different parts of the world. It was thirteen years before I went to Capri again.

My friend was still living on Capri, but he had moved into a smaller house. I stayed in a hotel. My friend had dinner with me in the hotel that night. And I asked him about his new house.

'You have been in the cottage,' my friend told me. 'It's the cottage that Thomas Wilson used to live in. I bought it. It's small, but comfortable.'

I had forgotten all about Wilson. Now I suddenly remembered him.

'What happened to Wilson?' I asked. 'Did he kill himself when he was sixty?'

'No, he didn't,' my friend replied. 'It's rather a sad story.

'When he reached the age of sixty, the money was finished. But he was able to borrow small sums of money. He told the owner of the cottage that his money would come soon. The owner's wife,

Assunta, came every day as usual. She cleaned the cottage and cooked his meals.

'He lived like this for over a year. In the end, the owner of the cottage told him he had to leave unless he paid the rent.

'That night, he tried to kill himself. He shut all the windows and lit a charcoal fire[22] in his bedroom. The next morning, Assunta came to make his breakfast. She found him lying on the bed. He was very ill, but he was still alive.

'They took him to hospital and he slowly got better. But he was not the same. I went to visit him in hospital. He didn't know who I was. Perhaps his mind was damaged by the smoke.'

'So what happened to him then?'

'Assunta helped him. She and her husband let him live in the woodshed behind their house. They give him food and he looks after their goats and their chickens.'

'It's not very comfortable in the woodshed,' my friend went on. 'Burning hot in the summer and freezing cold in the winter.'

'What does he do?' I asked.

'He walks in the hills on his own. I've tried to speak to him. But it's no good. He runs away whenever I go near him. Assunta comes down here sometimes to see me. I give her some money so that she can buy some tobacco for him. But I don't know if he gets the tobacco. Perhaps her husband takes the money and keeps it.'

'What a terrible way to live,' I said.

'It was Wilson's decision,' said my friend. 'He lived happily for twenty-five years. He didn't do any work. Why didn't he kill himself when he said he would?'

'It's not so easy to kill yourself,' I said. 'For a very long time, Wilson had lived an easy life. He had not had to make any decisions. When the time came to make a decision, he was unable to do anything.'

A few days later, I went for a walk with my friend. We were walking along a narrow path.

'There's Wilson!' my friend said suddenly.

I looked round and saw a man hiding behind a tree. He was like a wild animal. As soon as we had passed him, I heard him running away. That was the last time I saw him.

Wilson died last year. He had lived for six years in that woodshed. One morning they found his body on the hillside. It had been a full moon the night before.

Wilson had died in the moonlight. He died looking out over the beautiful bay of Naples that he loved so much.

I looked round and saw a man hiding behind a tree.

MABEL

I heard the story of George and Mabel when I was travelling in the Far East. I was sailing on a small ship from Pagan in Burma to Mandalay.

The ship stopped one night at a small riverside village. I was told that there was a small British club[23] there where I could spend the evening.

When I went into the club, I was welcomed by a tall, thin man whose face was burnt by the sun. We sat down and began to talk. While we were talking, another man came up to us. He told me that he was the club secretary[24].

'Hello, George,' he said to the tall, thin man. 'Have you had a letter from your wife yet?'

The man called George looked at the club secretary with a happy smile on his face.

'Yes, some letters arrived for me this morning,' he said. 'There was a long letter from my wife. She says she's enjoying her holiday.'

'Did she tell you not to worry?' asked the secretary.

'Yes, she did,' replied George. 'But I can't stop worrying. I'll be so glad when she's back here with me.'

Then he turned to me and went on, 'She's never been away from me before. I feel lost without her.'

'How long have you been married?' I asked him.

'Five minutes,' was George's immediate reply.

'Nonsense!' shouted the secretary with a loud laugh. 'You've been married eight years.'

George smiled. Then he looked at his watch. He said he had to go. He got up and left us.

The secretary watched him leave. Then he turned to me and

said, 'He feels terribly lonely since his wife went to England for a holiday. He misses his wife very much.'

'His wife must be very happy to know that her husband loves her so much,' I said.

'Mabel is a remarkable woman,' said the club secretary. And then he sat down in the chair beside me and told me the story of George and Mabel.

'George met Mabel when he was on holiday in England,' he began. 'They became engaged. They arranged to get married in Burma. George had to leave England immediately. Mabel planned to sail out to join him after six months.

'But Mabel wasn't able to leave England after six months. Mabel's father died. Then there was the War. In the end, Mabel had to wait for seven years. At last, she set out to join George in Burma.

'George made all the arrangements for the marriage. It was to take place on the day of her arrival. He travelled down to Rangoon to meet her. Mabel's ship was going to arrive in the morning. George went to the harbour to wait for her.

'He walked up and down. Then, suddenly, George became afraid. He had not seen Mabel for seven years. He had forgotten what she looked like!

'He did not know what to do. He did not know what he was going to say to her. He could not tell her that he had made a mistake. She had been engaged to him for seven years. She had come six thousand miles to marry him. What was he going to do?

'There was a ship in the harbour that was about to leave for Singapore. George decided to run away. He wrote a hurried note to Mabel and boarded the ship for Singapore.'

'What did he say in the note to Mabel?' I asked the secretary.

'He told her he had been called away on business. He didn't know when he would be back. He advised her to go back to England.'

'Did she take his advice?' I asked.

33

'He wrote a hurried note to Mabel and boarded the ship
for Singapore.'

'She did not,' replied the club secretary. 'When George arrived in Singapore, there was a cable[25] waiting for him.

I UNDERSTAND. DON'T WORRY.
LOVE. MABEL.

'George was sure that Mabel was following him. He got on a train that was leaving for Bangkok. When he got to Bangkok, he was still afraid. Perhaps she would follow him to Bangkok too. So he took a ship from Bangkok to Saigon. He was sure that Mabel would not follow him there.

'But he was wrong. When he booked in at the hotel, there was a telegram waiting for him. There were only two words in the telegram.

LOVE. MABEL.

'She was still following him!'
'What did he do next?' I asked.
'He left the hotel immediately and took a ship for Hong Kong. From Hong Kong, he went to Manila. From Manila, he went on to Shanghai. But he could not stay in Shanghai. Every time he went out of the hotel, he was afraid he would meet Mabel in the street. He went on to Yokohama.

'When he got to the hotel in Yokohama, there was a telegram waiting for him.

SORRY I MISSED YOU IN MANILA.
LOVE. MABEL.

'George did not know what to do. He decided to go back to Shanghai.

'He went straight to the British club. There was a telegram waiting for him.

ARRIVING SOON.
LOVE. MABEL.

'Then George had an idea. He knew how he could escape from Mabel. He decided to take a boat up the River Yangtze to Chungking. The Yangtze is a long river. Boats can only go up the Yangtze when there is enough water in the river. At that time, the water in the river was falling.

'George got on the last boat for Chungking. There wouldn't be another boat until the next spring. Only small boats could go on the river and a woman could not travel on them by herself. Mabel would not be able to follow him now.

'But George was still afraid. So when he got to Chungking, he decided to go further. He went four hundred miles by road to Cheng-tu, the capital of Szechuan. There were often robbers on that road and it was very dangerous. He was sure a woman would not travel on that road by herself.'

'George had escaped,' I said. 'He was safe there.'

'He thought he was,' replied the secretary. 'The British Consul[26] in Cheng-tu was a friend of George's. George stayed with him. The house was very comfortable and the weather was beautiful. George was able to rest after his long journey across Asia. He felt safe at last.

'One morning, George and the Consul were having breakfast. There was a loud knock on the wooden door. The door was pushed open and there stood Mabel!

'Mabel walked in looking cool and comfortable. George felt terrified. He looked as pale as death.

"Hello, George," said Mabel. "I'm glad you are still here. I was afraid that once again I would not find you."

"Hello, Mabel," George said quietly.

'That was all George was able to say,' the secretary went on. 'George looked to the left and he looked to the right. Mabel stood between him and the doorway.

37

'Mabel walked in looking cool and comfortable.'

"You haven't changed at all," she said to him. I've been so worried. I was afraid you would be fat and bald. It would have been terrible if I had not wanted to marry you after all these years."

'Mabel turned to George's friend.

"Are you the Consul?' she asked.

"I am."

"Good," she said. You can marry us. I'm ready to marry this man as soon as I've had a bath."

'And she did,' said the secretary.

39

THE WASH TUB

It was August. I was staying on the Island of Capri. The weather that year was beautiful. More and more visitors were arriving every day. My hotel became so crowded that I decided to go for a few days to Positano. I was sure that it would not be as busy and as crowded as Capri.

Positano is a small, very beautiful village on the Italian mainland. But the coast there is rocky and it is not easy to travel to Positano. The village is often busy in the winter. The small hotel is full of artists painting scenes of the coast. But Positano faces south. In the summer, it is very hot so few visitors go to Positano in August.

I had stayed in Positano before and I knew the waiter at the hotel. His name was Giuseppe. I asked Giuseppe if there were any other visitors staying at the hotel. He told me that there was only one other visitor – an American gentleman.

'Is he a painter or a writer?' I asked Giuseppe.

'No, he's not a painter or a writer,' replied Giuseppe. 'He's a rich gentleman. He's been here for three months. He reads and he goes swimming every day.'

'You'll meet the American in the restaurant down at the harbour,' Giuseppe told me. 'He always has his dinner there in the evening.'

When I arrived at the restaurant, it was empty. But a few minutes later, a tall, elderly man walked in. I knew immediately that this was the American Giuseppe had spoken about.

The American came straight to the table where I was sitting.

'Giuseppe has told me that you are staying at the hotel,' he said. 'May I join you for dinner?'

'Of course,' I replied. 'Please do join me.'

'May I join you for dinner?'

The American sat down and began to talk.

'I've been alone here for three months,' he said. 'This is the first time I have spoken English since I arrived.'

'Three months is a long time to stay at Positano,' I said. 'Don't you get bored?'

'I go out fishing and swimming every day. And I read. I've brought a lot of books with me. I can lend you a book if you want.'

'Thank you very much,' I replied. 'I've brought some of my own books with me. But I would like to see your books. It's interesting to see other people's books.'

After dinner, my American friend talked about many things. He spoke about art and about philosophy and his conversation was very interesting. I decided that he was a college professor. I asked him his name.

'Barnaby,' he replied.

'That is a name which has become very well-known in London this year,' I told him.

'Why is that?'

'Haven't you heard of the famous Mrs Barnaby? She's an American, like you.'

'Yes, I have heard of her,' my American friend replied. 'I've seen her name often in the newspapers. Do you know her?'

'I have met her often,' I said. 'She arrived in London in May and she gave some wonderful parties. I went to them whenever she asked me. All the fashionable[27] people in London go to her parties. Dukes, duchesses, lords and ladies, judges and Members of Parliament – all the important people go to her parties.'

'She's very rich, I believe,' said Barnaby.

'She is extremely rich,' I told him. 'But that is not why she has become so famous. She has become famous because of her amazing life. She tells the most interesting stories about herself and her husband.

'They were very poor when they were married and they lived with miners and cowboys[28]. Once, when they were very poor, they lived in a miners' camp. She did all the cooking for seventy miners. And she washed all their clothes in a wash tub[29]. Yes, she washed the clothes of seventy miners in that wash tub.'

My American friend smiled.

'Mrs Barnaby may be well-known in London,' he said. 'But she is completely unknown in America.'

'Did you know that in America her husband is called One–Bullet Mike?' I asked him.

'What a strange name!' he replied. 'How did he get that name?'

'Well, years ago, when they were living with cowboys, he killed two men with one bullet.'

'Like a hero in a Western film,' said my American friend, with a smile.

'Yes,' I said. 'A real hero. Everyone wants Mrs Barnaby to ask her husband to come to London. But she says that he won't. He won't leave Arizona. That's where he is happy.'

'So no one has met this amazing man?' said Barnaby.

'No one in London has met him,' I replied. 'But we have all heard such interesting stories about him. When he was a young man, he could not read or write. Then he found oil and he became very rich. He had to learn to write his name so that he could sign cheques[30].'

'How interesting,' said my American friend. 'What about Mrs Barnaby? Can she read and write?'

'The invitations to her parties are all written for her,' I replied. 'I don't know if she can write. But she taught herself to read. She used to read for an hour every night after the miners had gone to bed.'

'And after she had washed all their clothes in the wash tub,' said my American friend, with a smile. 'How amazing!'

'Yes,' I agreed. 'Her life has been really amazing.'

'They were very poor when they were married and they lived
with miners and cowboys.'

After dinner, we walked back to our hotel together. The next day, we went fishing in his boat. We had dinner together in the evening. Once again, I told my American friend stories about the amazing Mrs Barnaby and her amazing husband.

The following morning, after we had breakfast, I asked my American friend to show me his books.

'Come with me,' he said.

I followed him to his bedroom. Giuseppe was in the room. The first thing I saw was a photograph of Mrs Barnaby. It was placed on a table beside the bed. My friend saw the photograph at the same time as I did. He turned to Giuseppe.

'You're a fool, Giuseppe,' he said. 'Why did you take that photograph out of the cupboard? I put it there because I did not want anyone to see it.'

'I did not know that,' replied Giuseppe. 'I thought the signore would like to have the photograph of his signora beside his bed.'

Signore – signora, I thought to myself. Husband – wife.

I was amazed.

'Is Mrs Barnaby your wife?' I asked him.

'She is,' he replied.

'Then you are One-Bullet Mike!' I cried.

'Do I look like One-Bullet Mike?'

I had to laugh.

'No, you do not look like a cowboy,' I said.

'This is terrible,' he said. 'My wife will never forgive me. She wanted me to use a different name while I was here in Positano. But I would not. I said it was not necessary.'

'Please help me,' he went on. 'Please keep this secret to yourself. Please, do not tell anyone.'

'I will not tell anyone your secret,' I told him immediately. 'I will tell no one about this. But what does it mean? Why are you here in Positano while your wife is in London?'

'I'll tell you everything,' said Mr Barnaby. 'I am a doctor. For the past thirty years, my wife and I have lived quietly in

'Why did you take that photograph out of the cupboard?'

Pennsylvania. We were not rich. But we were not poor. And neither I nor my wife have ever lived with cowboys or miners.'

'But why . . .?' I began. But Mr Barnaby stopped me.

'Don't interrupt me,' he said. 'And I'll tell you the whole story. Last year, a cousin of Mrs Barnaby's died and left her a lot of money. That is the one thing about Mrs Barnaby which is true. My wife is an extremely rich woman.

'My wife had read many English novels. She had read about London and she wanted to live in fashionable London society. She now had enough money to do this. I did not want to go to London. But I agreed to go with her. We sailed to England last April.

'And that was where the trouble started – on the ship taking us to England. I was ill when the ship sailed and I had to stay in my cabin. My wife was on her own. And she made friends with the young Duke and Duchess of Hereford. They invited her to join them at their table in the dining-room.'

This time, I did interrupt him.

'I know about that,' I said. 'It was the Duke and Duchess of Hereford who introduced Mrs Barnaby into fashionable society. They told all their friends what an amazing woman she was. But why did they think that Mrs Barnaby was so interesting?'

'She told them stories,' replied Mr Barnaby. 'Let me explain. My wife is a clever woman. She listened to the Duke and Duchess talking about America. They had not enjoyed their visit to America. They had not met many interesting people.

'The Duke and Duchess had heard stories about the Wild West. But they had not met anyone from that part of America. So my wife told them a story about the Wild West. And to make the story more interesting she said that it had happened to her.

'The Duke and Duchess were amazed. They wanted to hear more. And my wife told them more – and more. And I helped her to think of the stories. Every evening, when she came back to our cabin, she told me about her success. And I helped her to think of another story for the following day.'

'But you have still not explained why you are here in Positano,' I reminded him.

'The day before we arrived in England, my wife asked me to help her. The Duke and Duchess liked her stories so much that they wanted to introduce her to all their friends.

'But there was a problem And I was the problem. I was the hero of all her stories. I had become One-Bullet Mike. But I did not look at all like One-Bullet Mike. If she introduced me to her friends, they would know the truth immediately. So I had to go away.

'I stayed in my cabin until the ship reached Cherbourg. I left the ship there and came here to Positano, as far away from London as possible.'

'So you never shot two men with one bullet?' I asked, feeling disappointed.

'I have never fired a gun in my life,' replied Mr Barnaby.

'But what about the wash tub?' I asked. 'What about washing clothes for seventy miners? We all thought that was a wonderful story.'

And I began to laugh.

'I still think she's a wonderful woman and I will never tell anyone your secret,' I said. 'She knows the kind of stories that people in London want to hear. You should be proud of her.'

'That's all right for you and the people of London,' said Mr Barnaby. 'But what about me? I have lost a good wife.'

'My dear Mr Barnaby,' I said, 'You cannot do anything about it. One-Bullet Mike must stay in the Wild West. You must stay here in Positano.'

'Thank you for your kind advice,' said Mr Barnaby.

But he said these words very coldly. I do not think he was thanking me at all.

POINTS
FOR
UNDERSTANDING

Points for Understanding

A MARRIAGE OF CONVENIENCE

1 The writer of these stories is Somerset Maugham. Somerset Maugham was on a ship when he first met the small Frenchman.
   (a) Where was the ship?
   (b) How did Somerset Maugham know that the man was a French Colonial Governor?
   (c) Describe the Governor and his wife.
2 How did Maugham know that the woman was very much in love with her husband?
3 'Monsieur,' the Governor began. 'Today is an important day in my life.'
   (a) Why was the day important?
   (b) Why was it very unusual?
4 Why did the Governor's wife think that it is better when love comes after marriage?
5 Why did the Frenchman have to get married?
6 The Frenchman advertised in a newspaper for a wife.
   (a) How many replies did he get to this advertisement?
   (b) What kind of ladies replied to his advertisement?
7 The Frenchman went to Geneva.
   (a) Why did he go there?
   (b) What did he take with him?
   (c) Why was he surprised when the door opened?
8 How did the meeting in Geneva end?
9 Why did the Governor advise Maugham to go to Geneva?
10 'Can you tell me the secret of your success?' asked Maugham.
   (a) Who replied to Maugham's question?
   (b) What was the reply?

GERMAN HARRY

1 A few days before he left Thursday Island, a man came up to Maugham in his hotel.
   (a) What was the man carrying?
   (b) Where did he want Maugham to take the things?
   (c) Who lived there?

2 What was unusual about German Harry?
3 The ship that German Harry worked on sank in a storm.
    (a)   How many men landed safely on the island of Trebucket?
    (b)   How many men were left when a ship came to save them?
    (c)   What had happened to the other men?
4 Why had German Harry refused to leave Trebucket?
5 Maugham remembered stories about men who had been left on islands where there was no food at all.
    (a)   Why were the stories horrible?
    (b)   What did Maugham think had perhaps happened to the other men on the island of Trebucket?
6 How was German Harry able to live on Trebucket?
7 German Harry lived alone on Trebucket for five years.
    (a)   Why did the pearl fishermen not come to Trebucket?
    (b)   Was German Harry interested when they told him why they had not come?
8 Why did the pearl fishermen try to make him drunk?
9 Why did Maugham want to meet this strange man?
10 Maugham met German Harry on Trebucket.
    (a)   What were German Harry's only interests?
    (b)   What one piece of news interested him?
    (c)   What had German Harry learnt during all those years alone on Trebucket?
11 'I knew what was going to happen,' said Maugham. What did Maugham think was going to happen?

THE LOTUS EATER

1 'I fell in love with this island the first moment I saw it,' Wilson told Maugham.
    (a)   Why did Wilson fall in love with Capri?
    (b)   What did he decide to do?
2 What was Wilson's one regret?
3 'But what about money?' Maugham asked Wilson.
    (a)   What did Wilson buy with his money?
    (b)   What did Wilson plan to do when he was sixty?
4 Describe the cottage where Wilson lived.
5 Who came to cook and clean for Wilson?

6 'I now knew everything about Wilson,' said Maugham.
    (a)   What did Maugham know about Wilson?
    (b)   What did Maugham think about Wilson's life?
7 When did Maugham visit Capri again?
8 Where was his friend living?
9 'When Wilson reached the age of sixty, the money was finished.'
    (a)   Did Wilson kill himself?
    (b)   What was Wilson able to do?
    (c)   How long did he live like this?
10 How did Wilson try to kill himself? Did he succeed?
11 How did Assunta help Wilson?
12 Maugham and his friend were out walking. What happened when they saw Wilson?
13 How did Wilson die?

MABEL

1 Where did George meet Mabel?
2 Where did they arrange to get married?
3 Mabel planned to sail out to join him after six months.
    (a)   Why was Mabel not able to leave England after six months?
    (b)   How long was it before she was able to set out to join George in Burma?
4 When was their marriage going to take place?
5 Then suddenly George became afraid.
    (a)   Why was George afraid?
    (b)   What did George decide to do?
6 George wrote Mabel a hurried note.
    (a)   What reason did George give Mabel for not waiting for her arrival?
    (b)   What did George advise Mabel to do?
7 What was waiting for George when he arrived in Singapore?
8 Where did George go to from Singapore?
9 Why was George afraid to go out on the streets in Shanghai?
10 Then George had an idea. He knew how he could escape from Mabel. What did George decide to do?
11 Who did George stay with in Cheng-tu?
12 Mabel walked in after her long journey following George. How did she look?
13 Why had Mabel been worried?
14 What was Mabel ready to do as soon as she had a bath?

THE WASH TUB

1 Why did Maugham decide to go to Positano?
2 Why did few visitors go to Positano in August?
3 Giuseppe told Maugham that there was only one other visitor staying in the hotel.
   (a) Who was Giuseppe?
   (b) Who was the other visitor?
   (c) Where would Maugham meet him?
4 The American sat down and began to talk straight away.
   (a) How long had the American been in Positano?
   (b) What did he do every day?
   (c) What did the American offer to lend Maugham?
5 The American's name was Barnaby.
   (a) Why was that name well-known in London?
   (b) Who went to Mrs Barnaby's parties?
6 Why had Mrs Barnaby become so famous?
7 'Once, when they were very poor, they lived in a miners' camp.'
   (a) How many miners lived in the camp?
   (b) How did Mrs Barnaby wash their clothes?
8 What was Mrs Barnaby's husband called in Arizona? Why?
9 Why did Mrs Barnaby's husband have to learn to write?
10 Maugham saw a photograph in the American's bedroom.
   (a) Whose photograph did he see?
   (b) Who was the American?
11 What was Mr Barnaby's reply when Maugham asked him if he was One-Bullet Mike?
12 Why was Mr Barnaby living in Positano?
13 Was the story about the wash tub true?
14 'One-Bullet Mike must stay in the Wild West,' Maugham told Mr Barnaby.
   (a) Where must Mr Barnaby stay?
   (b) Was Mr Barnaby really thanking Maugham for his advice?

GLOSSARY

Glossary

1 **boarded** (page 5)
   to board a ship is to get on a ship. When passengers are on the ship, they are on board.

2 **French Colonial Governor** (page 5)
   a colony is a country which is ruled by another country. At one time, France had many colonies in Africa and in the Far East. The Colonial Governor was sent from France to rule the country.

3 **cabins** (page 5)
   a cabin is a small room on a ship like a room in a hotel.

4 **deck** (page 5)
   the part of a ship where the passengers can walk about or sit down in the open air.

5 **anniversary** (page 6)
   your birthday is an example of an anniversary. It is the anniversary of the day on which you were born.

6 **bore** (page 6)
   to bore someone is to tell them a long story which does not interest them. A boring person is someone who tells long and uninteresting stories. To be bored is to have nothing interesting to do.

7 **a marriage of convenience** (page 6)
   when two people fall in love and get married, it is a marriage of love. But people can get married for other reasons. In this story, the Frenchman has to get married in order to get a job. He asks a woman to marry him, but he has never met the woman before. It is a marriage of convenience.

8 **interrupted** (page 6)
   to interrupt is to speak when someone else is speaking and to make the other person stop speaking.

9 **retired** (page 8)
   people retire when they stop working, usually when they become older. In many jobs, people must retire when they reach a certain age.

10 **Minister to the Colonies** (page 8)
   the person in the French Government who was in charge of all the colonies. It was the Minister's job to choose someone to be the Governor of a colony.

11   *advertisement* (page 8)
     a notice put in a newspaper. You can advertise something you
     want to buy or want to sell. In this case, the notice in the
     newspaper will say that the Frenchman wants to meet a woman
     who is ready to marry him.

12   *nervous* (page 11)
     to feel nervous is to feel worried or troubled. When you are
     nervous, your hands shake and you do not know what to say or do.

13   *respect* (page 14)
     to respect someone is to think well of them.

14   *pearl* (page 15)
     a valuable stone found inside a shellfish. Fishermen go down deep
     in the sea to find pearls.

15   *skipper* (page 15)
     the person in charge of a small ship.

16   *wrecked* (page 16)
     when a ship sinks in a storm or because it has hit a rock in the
     water, it is wrecked.

17   *turtle* (page 18)
     a large animal, with a shell on its back, which lives partly in the
     sea and partly on the land. It is good to eat.

18   *the Feast of the Assumption* (page 25)
     a Holy Day for Catholics. Catholics believe that the Virgin Mary
     did not die in an ordinary way. She was taken by God straight up
     to heaven. Catholics celebrate this Holy Day by walking through
     the streets carrying a statue of the Virgin Mary.

19   *regret* (page 25)
     to feel sad about something you have done.

20   *annuity* (page 26)
     you buy an annuity from an insurance company. The company
     then pays you some money every year until the money is finished.

21   *shed* (page 26)
     a small hut, usually made of wood.

22   *charcoal fire* (page 29)
     charcoal is made by baking wood in an oven. The smoke from a
     charcoal fire is dangerous. If someone breathes the smoke, they
     will become ill and possibly die.

23 **British club** (page 32)
the were many British colonies in Africa and the Far East. In a
British Colony there was usually a club where English people
could go. The club had a bar and a restaurant and a room where
people could sit and talk.

24 **club secretary** (page 32)
the club secretary was the person responsible for the running of
the club.

25 **cable** (page 36)
a message that is sent quickly from one place to another. At one
time, cables were sent along wires which went under the sea.
Today, most messages are sent quickly by radio or telephone.

26 **British Consul** (page 37)
the British Consul is a British official in a foreign country. The
Consul is able to marry British people living in that country.

27 **fashionable** (page 42)
fashionable people are well-known people who are usually rich
and important.

28 **cowboys** (page 43)
cowboys in America rode on horses and they looked after cattle
and other animals. They lived rough lives. There are many stories
and films about the lives of American cowboys.

29 **wash tub** (page 43)
a wash tub was a large wooden container in which clothes were
washed.

30 **cheques** (page 43)
when you put money into a bank, you are given a cheque book.
You pay bills with a cheque by writing the amount of money on
the cheque and signing the cheque.

W SOMERSET MAUGHAM
unsimplified

FICTION

Liza of Lambeth
Mrs Craddock
The Magician
Of Human Bondage
The Moon and Sixpence
The Trembling of a Leaf
On a Chinese Screen
The Painted Veil
The Casuarina Tree
Ashenden
The Gentleman in the Parlour
Cakes and Ale
First Person Singular
The Narrow Corner

Ah King
Don Fernando
Cosmopolitans
Theatre
The Summing Up
Christmas Holiday
Books and You
The Mixture as Before
Up at the Villa
Strictly Personal
The Razor's Edge
Then and Now
Creatures of Circumstance
Catalina

Here and There (*Collection of Short Stories*)
Quartet (*Four Short Stories with Film Scripts*)
A Writer's Notebook
Trio (*Three Short Stories with Film Scripts*)
The Complete Short Stories (3 *Vols.*)
Encore (*Three Short Stories with Film Scripts*)
The Vagrant Mood
The Collected Plays (3 *Vols.*)
The Selected Novels (3 *Vols.*)
The Partial View
Ten Novels and Their Authors
The Travel Books

INTERMEDIATE LEVEL

Shane *by Jack Schaefer*
Old Mali and the Boy *by D. R. Sherman*
Bristol Murder *by Philip Prowse*
Tales of Goha *by Leslie Caplan*
The Smuggler *by Piers Plowright*
The Pearl *by John Steinbeck*
Things Fall Apart *by Chinua Achebe*
The Woman Who Disappeared *by Philip Prowse*
The Moon is Down *by John Steinbeck*
A Town Like Alice *by Nevil Shute*
The Queen of Death *by John Milne*
Walkabout *by James Vance Marshall*
Meet Me in Istanbul *by Richard Chisholm*
The Great Gatsby *by F. Scott Fitzgerald*
The Space Invaders *by Geoffrey Matthews*
My Cousin Rachel *by Daphne du Maurier*
I'm the King of the Castle *by Susan Hill*
Dracula *by Bram Stoker*
The Sign of Four *by Sir Arthur Conan Doyle*
The Speckled Band and Other Stories by *Sir Arthur Conan Doyle*
The Eye of the Tiger *by Wilbur Smith*
The Queen of Spades and Other Stories *by Aleksandr Pushkin*
The Diamond Hunters *by Wilbur Smith*
When Rain Clouds Gather *by Bessie Head*
Banker *by Dick Francis*
No Longer at Ease *by Chinua Achebe*
The Franchise Affair *by Josephine Tey*
The Case of the Lonely Lady *by John Milne*

For further information on the full selection of
Readers at all five levels in the series, please refer
to the Heinemann Readers catalogue.

Macmillan Heinemann English Language Teaching
Betwwen Towns Road, Oxford OX4 3PP, UK
A division of Macmillan publishers limited
Companies and representatives throughout the world

ISBN O 435 27216 0

Heinemann is a registered trade mark of Reed Educational & ProfessionalPublishing Ltd

Theese stories were first published as a collection in 1951 by
William Heinemann Ltd in W. Somerset Maugham: *The
Complete Short Stories*
These retold versions for Heinemann ELT Guided Readers
© D. R. Hill 1988, 1992, 2001
First published 1998
Reprinted Twice
This edition published 2001

Illustrated by Paul Sullivan
Typography by Adrian Hodgkins
Cover by Janet Wooley and Threefold Design
Typeset in 11/12.5 pt Goudy
by Joshua Associates Ltd, Oxford
Printed and bound in Spain by Mateu Cromo, S.A.

2005 2004 2003 2002 2001
16 15 14 13 12 11 10 9 8 7